More than

70
Questions

PART

7
2020

Vibration Analysis Certification
Exam Preparation Package
Certified Vibration Analyst Category I

Acceptance Testing

Ali M. Al-Shurafa

Vibration Analysis Certification Exam Preparation Package Certified Vibration Analyst Category I
ACCEPTANCE TESTING CAT I PREP I SERIES PRACTICE TESTS FOR CVA (PART 7)
ISBN: 978-1-64415-004-7

Copyright © 2020

Disclaimers

Although every precaution has been taken to verify the accuracy of the information contained herein, the author and publisher assume no responsibility for any errors. No liability is assumed for damages that may result from the use of this package. The question banks in this booklet are related to the standard Body of Knowledge according to ISO standard 18436-2 Second Edition 2014.

Comments can be sent to info@prepcertify.com

Title	Vibration Analysis Certification Exam Preparation Package Certified Vibration Analyst Category I ACCEPTANCE TESTING	**Author**	Ali M. Al-Shurafa
Subtitle	ISO 18436-2 CVA LEVEL 1 PART 7	**Series**	CAT I PREP I SERIES PRACTICE TESTS
ISBN-10	1-64415-004-2	**ISBN-13**	978-1-64415-004-7
Publisher	Prep Certify	**Ordering**	www.prepcertify.com

Notes

TABLE OF CONTENTS

Notes

CAT I PREP I PACKAGE AND YOUR CERTIFICATION

Acceptance testing is basically an evaluation of a machine based on its vibration signature which can reflect possible abnormalities and categorize the level of risk. At Level 1 Vibration Certification, the primary risk considered is equipment damage due to vibration. The operational risks or downtime consequences are not covered in the evaluation. The outcome of acceptance testing is to state if the machine is healthy or not. After this step, there is a need for fault diagnosis (covered in Part 5 of this series). The corrective action is specified based on the diagnosed fault. Regardless of exact criteria, all of acceptance tests primarily depend on the vibration amplitude.

In this booklet, a major focus is on making sense of the concept of severity evaluation. You will need to compare the vibration reading collected from the equipment to predefined criteria. Usually, the criteria value are referred to as limits or set points.

Regardless of the set point format, value or the objective, the measured vibration level must be lower than the set point to accept the machine.

The evaluation result is acceptance if the reading is below the set point, as shown in Figure 1.

Vibration Readings < Set Point

To obtain the best outcome from vibration analysis of a machine, the analyst needs to take the measurement and present that measurement in an appropriate form like single simple number (e.g. overall) or a plot (e.g. trend). In real world and exam, you may need to extract the amplitude from a vibration plot, which can be a waveform or spectrum. You might need also to find the vibration frequency or shaft speed. Be careful about the method of amplitude measurement specially if the evaluation is based on a spectrum. Mistakes happen if the analyst mixes between mm/s 0-p and mm/s rms, for example.

Early abnormality detection is a key objective of applying vibration technology on machinery, in order to reduce the risk of machine's damage and operational downtime (planned and unplanned). Vibration is a very good application for the P-F curve to improve uptime and optimize maintenance resources. (Figure 2). The earlier the fault is detected, the easier to handle the case and plan for the repair. If equipment breaks down while it is under a vibration-monitoring program, this event uncovers two failures:

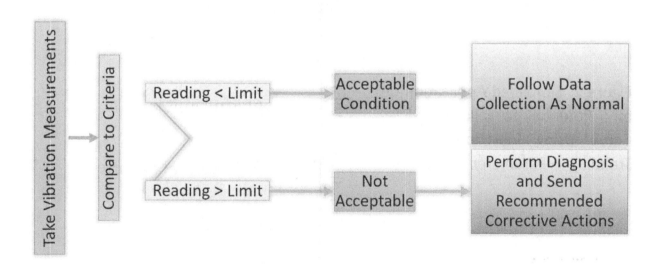

Figure 1 Acceptance Test Results

Figure 2 Simplified Application for Potential to Failure P-F Curve Using Vibration as a Trending Parameter

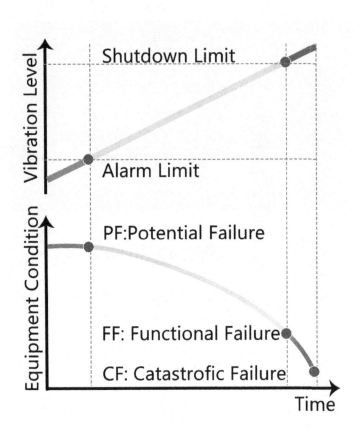

1) a physical damage on the equipment and
2) a systemic failure on the vibration program.

Late detection of a failure of a machine is a failure (by itself) of the vibration monitoring program. Not all faults are detectable by vibration, however.

Mature condition monitoring programs employ as many variables as needed. They would include vibration, bearing temperature, lube oil tests, noise etc. In this booklet, the focus is limited on vibration (overall and 1X amplitudes).

During acceptance testing, a new machine is treated differently from an old machine or a machine after repair. In general, the acceptance requirements are more stringent for new and repaired assets than those for others. Refer to Figure 3 and Figure 4 for simplified classification of vibration set point.

For contractual reasons, set points must be agreed on ahead of time so when the run test is conducted, no dispute is developed. Many times, this part of the "contract" is not given the full attention. Invalid assumptions about acceptance test details lead to disagreements during the evaluation when one party rejects the equipment or the test procedure.

Two common examples of pitfalls or discrepancies in acceptance tests are:

1- Equipment vendor uses rms method of amplitude calculation while equipment owner uses 0-p for case vibration measurements.

2- Operations staff use the vibration readings from the online system while the vibration technician uses the portable data collector's readings.

In real world, the evaluation of vibration is done based multiple readings. For example, the vibration analyst takes three readings per bearing and the measurements might be repeated to ensure the stability of the condition. The maximum or latest reading is usually considered for the evaluation. The acceptance criterion can be a single value, however, it also can be given in a generic chart from which you need to identify the applicable set point for your specific case. Such charts or tables contain multiple set points for different cases. In such cases during your exam, read the question for related hints to your application such as the type of sensor or type of bearing.

For example, usually, small machines use rolling element bearings and as a result casing measurement is used with velocity in most cases. On the contrary, large machines like steam turbines and generators use journal bearings. Another hint is that typically if the sensor is a

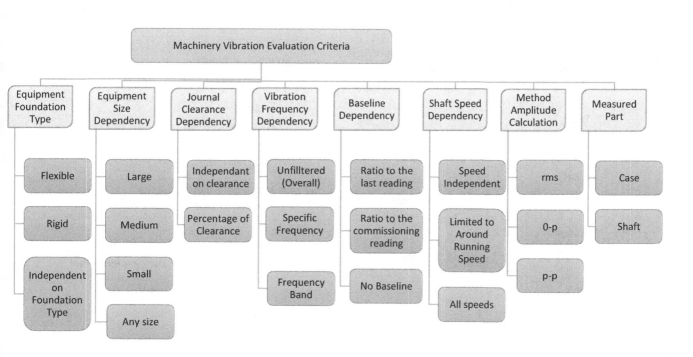

Figure 3 Classifications of Acceptance Criteria and Potential Pitfalls for Using Vibration Set Points

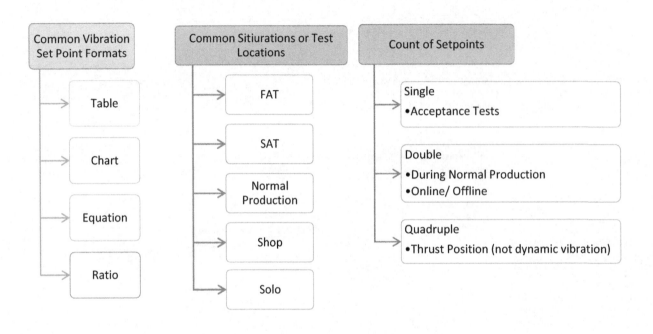

Figure 4: Vibration Set Point Format, Location and Count

a relative probe, the vibration must be for the shaft and the measured amplitude is in displacement, mils (or μm) pp. Study the tables given in the Formula Sheet section before proceeding to the Question Bank.

Part 7 contains 79 practice questions. Many questions are challenging to what a formal Category I analyst would be trained on and these questions are marked using the icon at the end of the question.

Good luck, Ali M. Al-Shurafa

CAT I BODY OF KNOWLEDGE

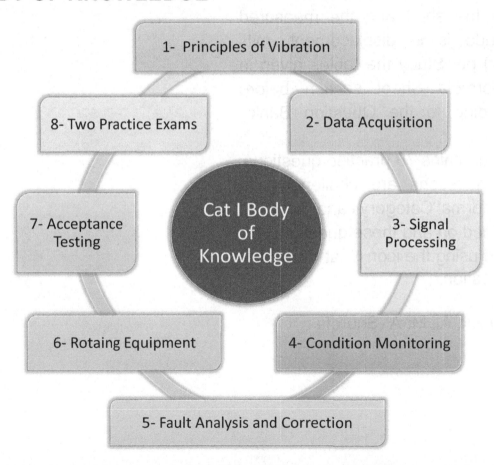

CAT I PART 7 BODY OF KNOWLEDGE

Below details are the Body of Knowledge as specified by ISO standard 18436-2 for Part 7 "Acceptance Testing". For a complete list of topics, refer to Part 8 or the standard.

Topic	Details
Test procedure	Be able to apply basic pre-set methods, and be aware of access and safety requirements

FORMULA SHEET FOR CAT I PREP I PART 7

Table 1 Typical Severity Evaluation Table for Shaft Vibration for Large Machines

Vibration Severity	Shaft Vibration To Bearing Clearance Ratio = R/C*		Recommended Action
	Low Speed 0 - 3600 rpm	High Speed 3601 - 10000 rpm	
Normal	Less than 0.3	Less than 0.2	Routine Monitoring
Surveillance	0.3 - 0.5	0.2 - 0.4	Diagnose and Increase Monitoring
Critical	0.5 - 0.7	0.4 - 0.6	Plan for a Shutdown
Dangerous	More than 0.7	More than 0.6	Shutdown Immediately

*R is the relative overall shaft vibration amplitude (in mils or um).

C is the dramatic clearance (in mils or um) between the shaft and bearing.

Table 2 Typical severity evaluation table for vibration collected from equipment's bearing housing for faults covered by operating speeds. Frequency covered is typically up to 20X shaft speed.

Condition	Overall Vibration Amplitude (inch per second)		Overall Vibration Amplitude (mm per second)		Recommended Action
	RMS	PEAK	RMS	PEAK	
Like New	< 0.08	< 0.16	< 2.0	< 4.1	Routine Monitoring
Normal	0.8 to 0.12	0.16 to 0.24	2.0 to 3.1	4.1 to 6.1	
Surveillance	0.12 to 0.28	0.24 to 0.70	3.1 to 6.1	6.1 to 17.8	Troubleshoot
Unacceptable	> 0.28	> 0.70	> 6.1	> 17.8	Shutdown

Type of Machine				Vibration Amplitude	
Small Machines < 15 kW	Medium Machines 15 < kW < 75	Large Machines > 75 kW — Heavy/Normal foundation	Large Machines > 75 kW — Special foundation	Velocity (inches/sec rms)	Velocity (mm/sec rms)
Unacceptable	Unacceptable	Unacceptable	Unacceptable	1.77	44.958
Unacceptable	Unacceptable	Unacceptable	Unacceptable	1.1	27.94
Unacceptable	Unacceptable	Unacceptable	Unsatisfactory	0.71	18.034
Unacceptable	Unacceptable	Unsatisfactory	Unsatisfactory	0.48	12.192
Unacceptable	Unsatisfactory	Unsatisfactory	Satisfactory	0.28	7.112
Unsatisfactory	Unsatisfactory	Satisfactory	Satisfactory	0.18	4.572
Unsatisfactory	Satisfactory	Satisfactory	Good	0.11	2.8
Satisfactory	Satisfactory	Good	Good	0.07	1.778
Satisfactory	Good	Good	Good	0.04	1.016
Good	Good	Good	Good	0.03	0.75
Good	Good	Good	Good	0.02	0.508
Good	Good	Good	Good	0.01	0.254

Table 3 Simplifed criteria for vibration evlaution based on the concept of ISO 10816-3 Mechanical vibration- Evaluation of machine vibration by measurements on non-rotating parts- Part 3: Industrial machines with nominal power above 15 kW and nominal speeds between 120 r/min and 15 000 r/min when measured in situ.

More than
70
Questions
PART
7
2020

QUESTION BANK

Acceptance Testing

Ali M. Al-Shurafa

Acceptance Testing
Question 001

How does an analyst use vibration data to evaluate the condition of a machine? Select the best option.

A. By comparing the measured amplitude to predefined alarm/trip set points.

B. By converting the measured waveform to a spectrum using FFT.

C. By comparing the measured frequency of 1X to the shaft's running speed.

D. By applying the correct low pass and high pass filters.

Note : ....

....

....

In the field of machinery vibration analysis, what is the difference between acceptance testing and condition monitoring?

	Acceptance Testing is _____.	Condition Monitoring is _____.
A.	conducted for two parties like equipment vendor and owner. The purpose is to ensure contract compliance	a routine data collection to detect a quantitative change in the condition of the machine
B.	usually based on a single limit (e.g. acceptable set point)	usually based on two limits (e.g. alert and danger)
C.	performed primarily using casing vibration measurements	performed primarely using online shaft vibrations
D.	A and B	

Acceptance Testing
Question 003

> Consider a typical machine that has been returned to the plant's site from a repair shop. When is it required to collect the vibration data in order to give a reliable condition evaluation and detect faults?

A. During the first start (first a few minutes)

B. After operating parameters stabilize (first a few hours)

C. After a few days of continuous operation

D. All of the above

Note : ....

....

....

Acceptance Testing
Question **004**

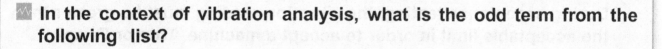

In the context of vibration analysis, what is the odd term from the following list?

A. Vibration assessment

B. Severity evaluation/ determination

C. Fault diagnosis

D. Acceptance testing

Note : ....

....

....

Acceptance Testing
Question 005

During acceptance testing, the vibration reading must be greater than the acceptable limit in order to accept a machine. True or False?

A. True, this is especially true for new machines.

B. True, this is especially true if the machine has been in service.

C. False. For healthy equipment, the acceptance limit must be larger than the reading.

D. False, there is no such a rule. Machine acceptance is decided by the OEM or a vendor's representative.

Note : ....

....

....

The overall vibration readings must be zero in order to accept a new machine under evaluation. True or False?

A. True, except for new reciprocating machines whose reading is above zero by nature.

B. True. New machines are expected to have a very smooth vibration (zero).

C. False. Both acceptance limit and vibration reading must be above zero, in all cases. Furthermore, overall and filtered amplitudes are awlyas positive.

D. False. Both acceptance limit and vibration reading must be negative, similar to the gap voltage. However, for simplicity the negative sign is dropped.

Note : ....

....

....

Acceptance Testing
Question 007

Assume that you conducted an acceptance test which concluded that a machine is rejected because its vibration is greater than the limit. What is the next step during normal cases? Select the best choice from the given answers.

A. Report the result and then start diagnosis if required.

B. Give a recommendation to replace the defective parts.

C. Start vibration reduction by implementing the easy repair options like shaft alignment.

D. Start vibration reduction by implementing the cost effective repair options like bearing greasing.

Note : ....

....

....

Acceptance Testing
Question 008

To whom/where does an analyst need to refer in order to know the proper vibration limits of the rotating machines at the facility?

A. OEM machine's documents such as data sheets and manuals

B. Reports/recommendations from the plant's machinery specialist

C. Manufacturer of the online vibration monitoring system connected to these machines

D. A and B

Note : ....

....

....

Acceptance Testing
Question 009

Assume you follow certain vibration limits (Alarm and Danger) for a condition monitoring (route) program to evaluate rotating equipment. Can these limits be changed?

A. Yes, if necessary. However, the change is done after an evaluation by a qualified person or team.

B. Yes, it is done if the vibration reading is high for three (3) consecutive measurements.

C. No. A vibration limit is extremely dangerous to change.

D. No, in general, except if the bearing manufacturer allows this change. Usually, bearing manufacturers don't allow.

Assume that your company has purchased a major rotating machine. During the acceptance test witnessed by the buyer and vendor, how many limits are used for vibration evaluation?

A. One: acceptable

B. Two: low and high

C. Two: high and high-high

D. Two: warning and danger

Note : ....

....

....

Acceptance Testing
Question 011

A vibration signal is generally described by its amplitude, frequency and phase. However, vibration severity of a machine is mostly dependent on the amplitude. True or False?

A. True. Most severity charts, formulae etc. primarily focus on amplitudes to assess or determine the condition of the machine.

B. True. Furthermore, the higher the measured amplitude, the lower the severity of the vibration.

C. False. Vibration frequency is by far more important than the amplitude when it comes to condition evaluation for rotating equipment.

D. False. Shaft speed and phase are the most important parameters when it comes to condition evaluation for rotating equipment.

The vibration severity of a machine changes if the measured vibration amplitude is converted from displacement to velocity or acceleration. In other words, the risk of equipment's damage changes if the vibration amplitude is converted from mils (µm) to in/sec (mm/sec) or g. True or False?

A. True because velocity vibration is stronger than displacement.

B. True because measured vibration amplitudes increase after conversion.

C. False because measured vibration amplitudes decrease after conversion.

D. False. The physical level of a vibration and its severity (to damage the equipment) remain unchanged before and after conversion.

Note :

Acceptance Testing
Question 013

Study the below vibration data to evlaute the condition of a machine. What is the most important parameter, indicated by letter, to consider for the evaluation?

A. Period

B. Amplitude scale

C. Time span

D. Highest amplitude

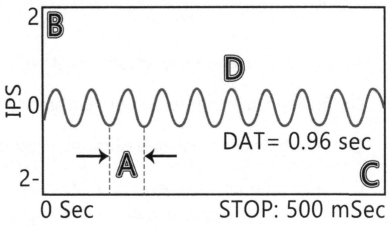

Note : ....

....

....

Study the below vibration data to evlaute the health of a machine. What is the most important parameter, indicated by letter, to consider for the evaluation?

A. Filtered amplitudes

B. Amplitude scale

C. Frequency span

D. Overall amplitude

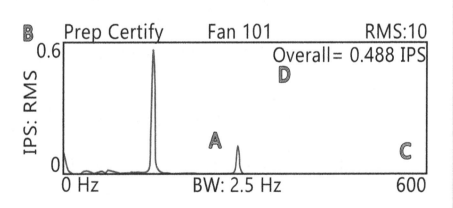

Note : ....

....

....

Acceptance Testing
Question 015

Consider a machine whose rotor is mounted on fluid film bearings. Vibration severity is evaluated more accurately when the vibration of the shaft is expressed in velocity. True or False?

A. True. Vibration in velocity is more accurate and much easier to evaluate. Velocity in ips or mm/s is commonly used.

B. True. Unifying shaft and case vibration units (in velocity rms or 0-P) is a best practice for accurate assessments.

C. True. In fact, the gap voltage (of shaft measurement) reflects the shaft's velocity. It is given in VDC.

D. False. Shaft vibration is commonly measured and more accurately evaluated in displacement.

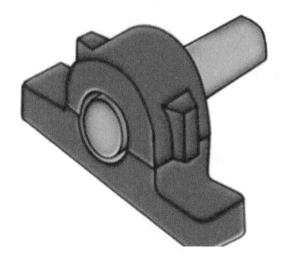

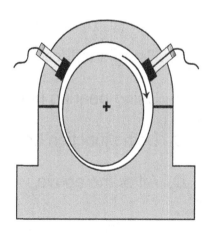

Note : ....

....

....

Acceptance Testing
Question 016

Consider a large horizontal induction motor (5000 hp or 3730 kW) whose rotor is mounted on journal bearings. Based on this limited information, what is the best method to evaluate the vibration severity of this motor?

A. Using shaft (relative) vibration amplitude

B. Using bearing housing (absolute) vibration frequency

C. Using junction box (absolute) vibration phase

D. All of the above

A 2000 Hp (1490 kW) horizontal pump (6 vanes) operating at 990 rpm is mounted on fluid film bearings. It is under monitoring using an online system, however, this pump does not have an online tachometer. What is most likely the best vibration measure to evaluate the pump's vibration condition? Select the best choice from the given answers.

A. Displacement measured by a relative probe system

B. Velocity measured by a bearing case sensor system

C. Acceleration measured by a bearing housing transducer system

D. Impossible to know the answer without measuring the speed by a tachometer.

Note : ....

....

....

Acceptance Testing
Question 018

Assume you are a new analyst at a plant where online vibration monitors are installed inside a building. Do you need to ask for a work permit prior to taking data from an online vibration monitoring system by a vibration analyzer?

A. Yes, in general. This is a common practice in many plants and the industry.

B. Yes, unless the online system is for a critical machine (higher than 500 HP or 375 kW).

C. No, because the vibration data collection from online monitors doesn't involve tangible safety risks.

D. No, because work permit is needed only for jobs performed at the field.

Do you need to get a work permit prior to taking vibration data? Assume you want to survey a pump at the site by a portable analyzer at an industrial facility.

A. Yes, in general. This is a common practice in many plants and the industry.

B. Yes, except if the survey is for a large machine (higher than 500 Hp or 375 kW).

C. No. Vibration data collection does not cause machine shutdown even if the collected reading is high.

D. No. Work permit is needed only for hard jobs at the field (like mechanical, electrical, piping etc.).

Note : ....

....

....

Acceptance Testing
Question 020

Assume you are a vibration analyst performing acceptance tests. You have collected vibration data of a new large pump from an online rack installed in a remote control room. You also need to visit the machine on the site to evaluate its condition. True or False?

A. False, because both rack and field measurements end up with the same evaluation.

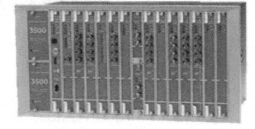

Rack Example (Bently Nevada)

B. True. Rack measurements can be incorrect specially for new machines.

C. True. Rack measurements do not detect all critical abnormalities/ problems encountered by the equipment.

D. B and C.

Consider a healthy rotating equipment under evaluation. What is the effect of changing operating conditions (e.g. increasing or decreasing the speed or load) on the machine's vibration?

A. Generally speaking, as the load (or speed) increases, the vibration increases.

B. Generally speaking, as the load (or speed) increases, the vibration decreases.

C. For healthy machines, the vibration remains constant regardless of increasing or decreasing the load/speed.

D. There is no simple or generic relation between load/speed and vibration.

Note : ....

....

....

Acceptance Testing
Question 022

> Which statement is true about the overall vibration? Select the best choice from the given answers.

A. Overall level is a very basic, useful and practical way to evaluate the condition of rotating equipment.

B. The overall vibration amplitude is the resultant of all vibration components. It is not a good evaluation parameter.

C. The overall vibration amplitude is only possible to measure using advanced instruments.

D. The overall vibration trend is the main analysis plot used for fault diagnosis.

Note : ....

....

....

Acceptance Testing
Question **023**

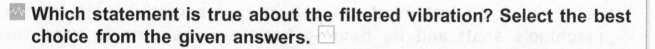

Which statement is true about the filtered vibration? Select the best choice from the given answers.

A. Filtered amplitudes can be more critical (in specific cases) than the overall amplitudes.

B. Using filtered vibration amplitudes is the most common method for severity evaluation during fast screening of large sets of mchines.

C. Most modern online protection systems use filtered amplitudes to trip the machines.

D. Filtered vibration amplitudes are possible to measure only using the online vibration systems.

Note : ....

....

....

Question 024

A vibration analyst needs to collect representative data from a machine's shaft and its bearing housing. The data is used for acceptance testing. What are typical frequency ranges used for shaft and bearing case vibrations when they are expressed in displacement? X refers to shaft running speed. Select the best choice from the given options.

	Shaft Displacement Frequency Range	Case Structural Displacement Frequency Range
A.	0 - 0.1 X	0 - 5000 X
B.	0 - 1 X	0 - 500 X
C.	0 - 10 X	0 - 50 X
D.	0 - 100 X	0 - 5 X

You need to collect good quality vibration data that contains the frequencies of the common machinery vibration problems. Which of the following could be typical frequency ranges used for velocity and acceleration? X refers to shaft running speed. Select the best choice from the given answers.

	Frequency Range of Bearing Housing Vibration	
	Velocity	Acceleration
A.	0 - 5 X	0 - 400 X
B.	0 - 50 X	0 - 100 X
C.	0 - 0.5 X	0 - 40 X
D.	0 - 500 X	0 - 10 X

Acceptance Testing
Question 026

In acceptance testing, is the analyst expected to report the results of the test if the vibration amplitude is very low? In this context, consider the following as very low amplitudes: 0.02 ips 0-p and 0.05 mm/sec 0-p.

A. Yes, in general. Low or high amplitude and other required data must be reported.

B. No need to report low amplitudes. It does not matter how low (below the limit) the vibration is.

C. No need to report low amplitude. The analyst needs to report only the high vibration data.

D. B and C

Consider vibration data that is collected at the site from a typical motor-pump unit with an abnormality. What should and should not a vibration analyst touch and smell in order to understand the abnormalities or defects within the unit? Select the best choice from the given answers.

A. There is no general answer for this question. The analyst needs to follow the applicable safety rules in that specific site/ facility.

B. Bearing housings can always be touched to verify the temperature and vibration.

C. Touching the shaft by hand is recommended prior to the analysis, provided that the speed is low and a strobe light is used.

D. Touching pump or motor cases to verify the readings is a best practice. Also, smelling and touching seals on the pump side are recommended.

Acceptance Testing
Question 028

A low power gearbox has a gear mesh frequency of 1622 Hz while its input shaft's speed is 3550 rpm. The shafts are mounted on ball bearings. What vibration measures are suitable to perform acceptance test for this machine?

A. Case displacement and shaft velocity

B. Shaft displacement and shaft acceleration

C. Case displacement and gap voltage

D. Case velocity and case acceleration

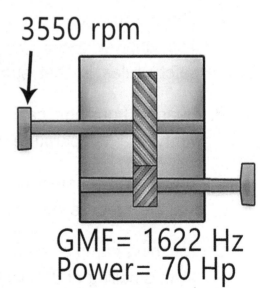

3550 rpm

GMF= 1622 Hz
Power= 70 Hp

Study the next waveform. What are the 0-p and p-p amplitudes? The total Data Acquisition Time = 960 mseconds. Hint: use a ruler for accurate answers. Expect some rounding.

	mm/s Zero-Peak	mm/s Peak-Peak
A.	3	1.5
B.	1.2	0.85
C.	1.2	2.5
D.	4.9	9.75

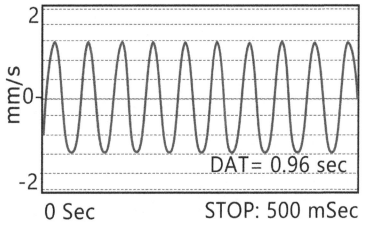

Note : ....

....

....

Acceptance Testing
Question 030

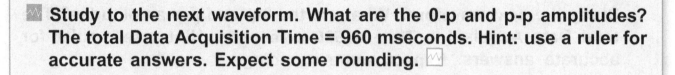 **Study to the next waveform. What are the 0-p and p-p amplitudes? The total Data Acquisition Time = 960 mseconds. Hint: use a ruler for accurate answers. Expect some rounding.**

	IPS Zero-Peak	IPS Peak-Peak
A.	0.02	0.04
B.	0.22	0.46
C.	0.42	0.84
D.	0.96	1.92

Note : ....

....

....

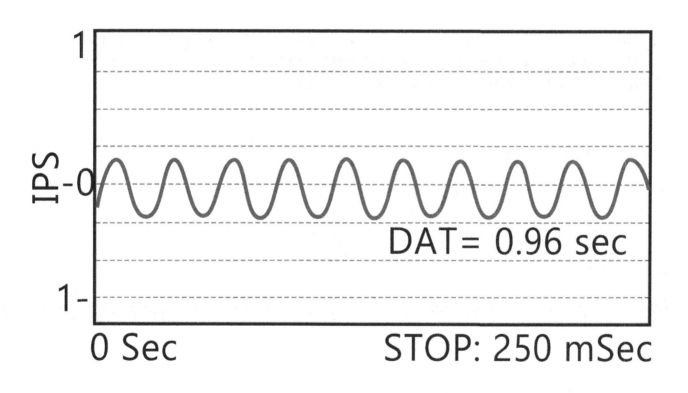

Acceptance Testing
Question 031

Study to the next waveform. What are the 0-p and p-p amplitudes? Hint: use a ruler for accurate answers. Expect some rounding. Select the best answer from the given options.

	Peak	Peak-Peak
A.	1.0 mil	2.5 mil
B.	0.33 mil	0.67 mil
C.	0.5 ips	0.8 ips
D.	10 cycles	20 cycles

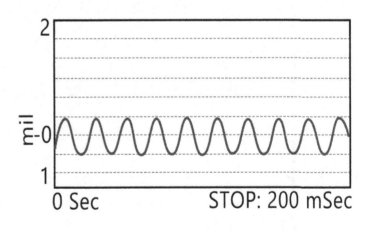

Note : ....

....

....

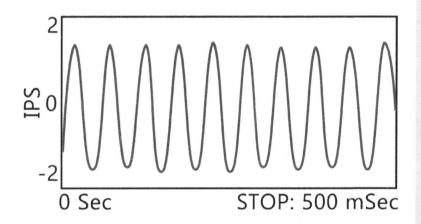 **Study the next waveform. What is the rms amplitude? Hint: use a ruler for accurate answers. Expect some rounding.**

	IPS RMS
A.	0.020
B.	0.31
C.	0.679
D.	1.1

Note :

Acceptance Testing
Question 033

You are asked to evaluate the condition of a pump under an acceptance test, using the next vibration data? What is the overall amplitude expressed in peak, peak to peak and rms? Consider some approximation and select the best option.

	ips 0-p	ips p-p	ips rms
A.	0.14	0.24	0.10
B.	0.16	0.32	0.22
C.	0.23	0.40	0.17
D.	0.29	0.55	0.15

Note : ....

....

....

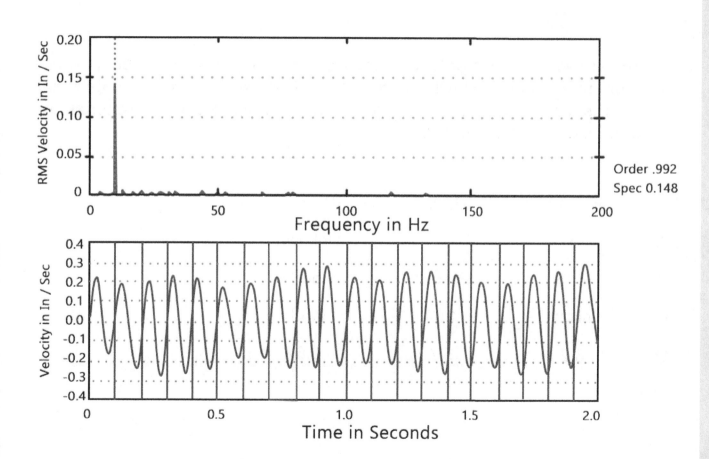

Order .992
Spec 0.148

Acceptance Testing
Question 034

You are asked to evaluate the condition of a pump under an acceptance test, using the next vibration data? What is the overall amplitude expressed in peak, peak to peak and rms? Expect some approximation and select the best option.

	IPS 0-p	IPS p-p	IPS rms
A.	3	7	Unkown
B.	2.46	Unkown	0.5804
C.	Unkown	1.64	0.58
D.	3.2	5.7	0.6

Note : ....

....

....

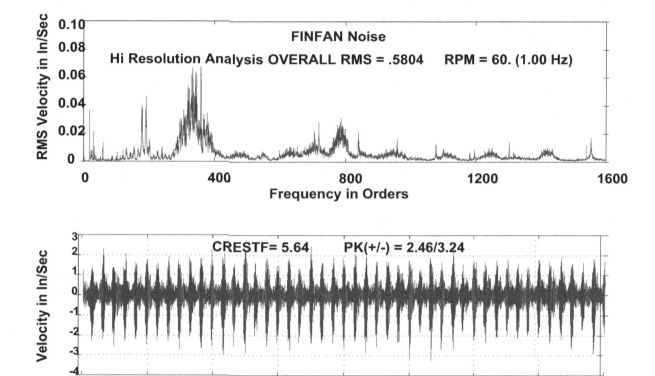

Acceptance Testing
Question 035

Study the vibration plots. What is the amplitude of 1X and the overall vibration?

	Mil p-p	
	1X	Overall
A.	0.9	1.8
B.	0.8	-0.9
C.	-0.9	Unkown
D.	Unknown	1.8

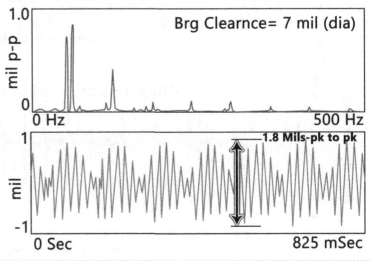

Note : ....

Which plot is the best (most preferred) to use in order to accurately calculate the overall velocity vibration in zero to peak values? Sometimes, this value is referred to as true peak.

A. Displacement gap voltage trend

B. Velocity time waveform

C. Velocity shaft centerline

D. Acceleration spectrum

Note :

Question 037

Which plot is the best to use (most preferred) in order to accurately calculate the overall vibration displacement in peak to peak values? Displacement pp is common with journal bearings.

A. Displacement time waveform

B. Velocity time waveform

C. Velocity gap voltage trend

D. Shaft axial position in mil (micron)

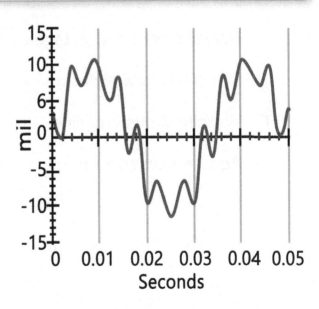

The following waveforms are collected from sister machines. Which of them is the worse in terms of vibration severity?

A.	Plot 1 is worse.	C.	They are at the same severity
B.	Plot 2 is worse.	D.	It depends on the value of the critical speed.

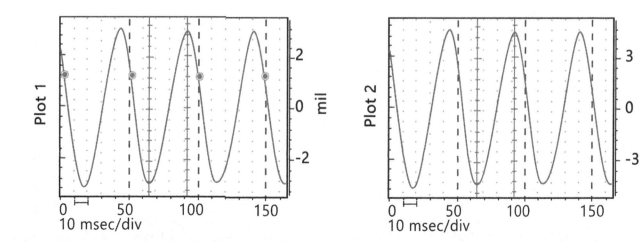

Acceptance Testing
Question 039

The following waveforms are collected from sister small machines with ball bearings. The data covers one complete shaft rotation. Based on this limited information, which plot is most likely the worst in terms of vibration severity?

A.	Plot 1	C.	They are identical
B.	Plot 2	D.	No way to tell without knowing the speed.

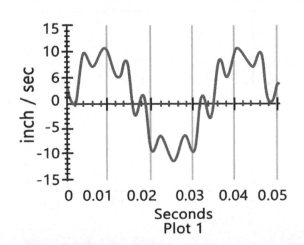

Plot 1

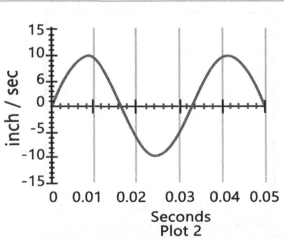

Plot 2

The following seismic spectra are collected from sister machines in a power plant. Which of them is the worst in terms of vibration severity?

A.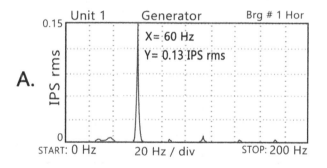

B.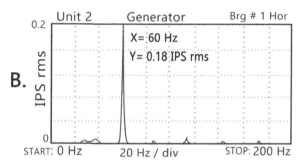

C.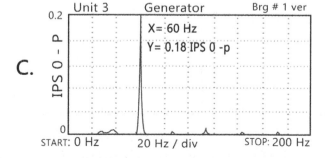

D.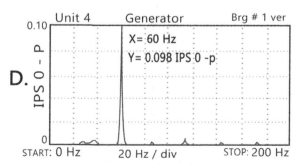

Question 041

The following overall vibration trends are collected from sister motors by an online system. Which plot shows the smoothest vibration? All signatures contain 2LF as the dominant peak.

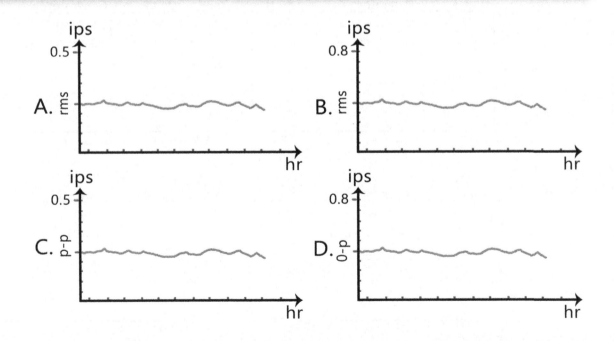

The following trends are collected from sister pumps by an online system. Which case is the worst in terms of vibration severity? All signitures contain major 1X amplitudes.

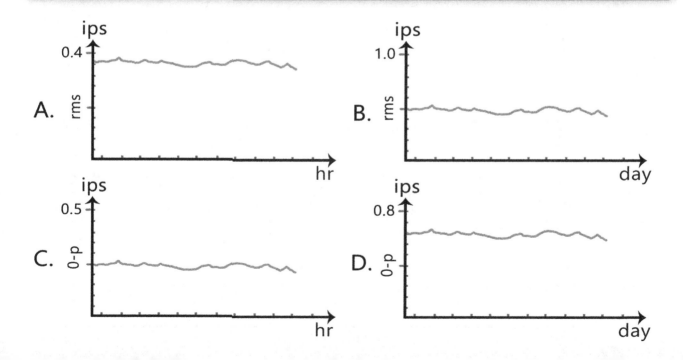

Acceptance Testing
Question 043

The following trends are collected from sister machines by an online system. Which plot is the worst in terms of vibration severity? All waveform signatures contain a major vibration signal component at 50 Hz.

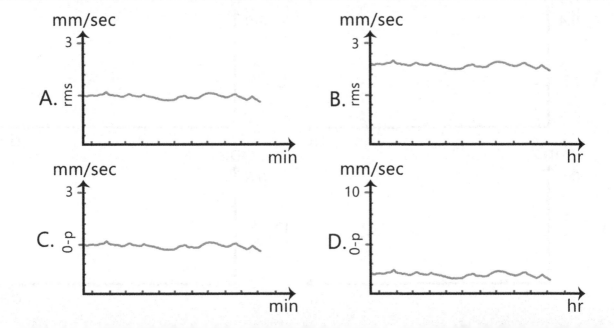

Which waveform most likely demonstrates the worst vibration condition? Consider: 1 ips = 25 mm/s.

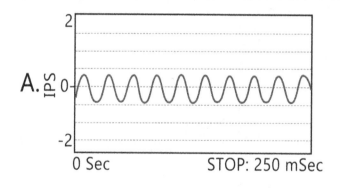

A.

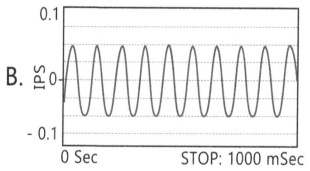

B.

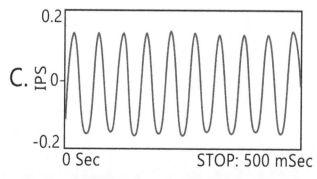

C.

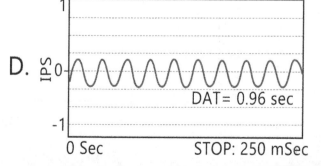

D.

Acceptance Testing
Question 045

Which spectrum most likely demonstrates the worst condition in term of vibration severity?

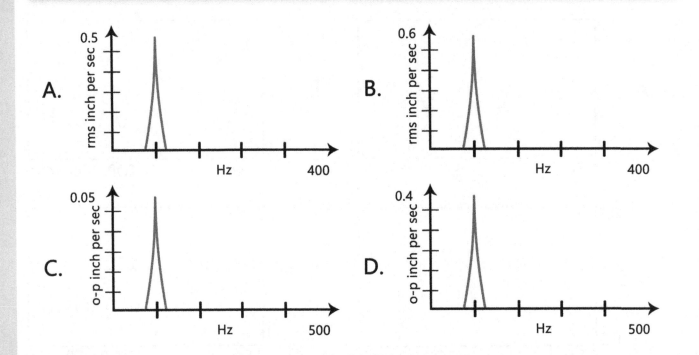

Consider a small size (10 Hp or 7.5 kW) motor running at 1780 rpm. What is the evaluation of a vibration amplitude of this motor at 0.23 ips rms which is mostly at 1X? Use Table 1.

A. Normal

B. Surveillance

C. Unacceptable

D. Unknown. It depends on the natural frequency

Table 1 MACHINE SEVERITY	Overall Vibration Severity Guide for Operating Speed Faults (inch per second)
	RMS
Acceptable	Less than 0.08
Normal	0.08 to 0.12
Surveillance	0.12 to 0.28
Unacceptable	More than 0.28

Acceptance Testing
Question 047

Which plot demonstrates the worst condition in term of overall vibration severity? Plot 1 and Plot 2 were taken from the same machine using the same setup but at different times. Hint: For accurate amplitudes, use a ruler.

A. Plot 1

B. Plot 2

C. Impossible to tell. The lines of resolution is required to know.

D. They have very similar evaluation

Note : ....

....

....

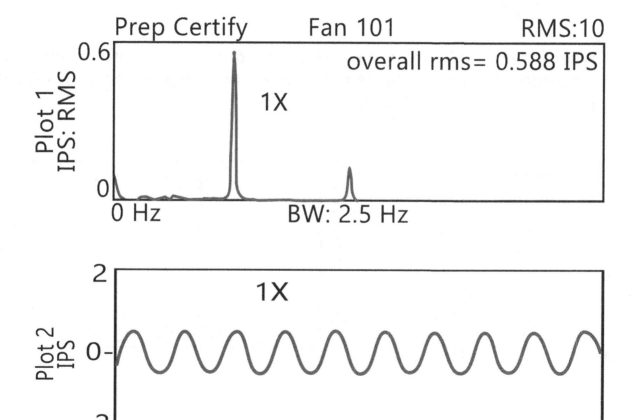

Prep Certify   Fan 101   RMS:10

overall rms= 0.588 IPS

Plot 1
IPS: RMS

0.6

1X

0

0 Hz   BW: 2.5 Hz

Plot 2
IPS

2

1X

0

-2

0 Sec

Question 048

What is the amplitude of the next shaft vibration waveform taken from a centrifugal pump? What is the condition of the pump? Alarm = 6 mil p-p. Select the best answer.

	Amplitude (mil p-p)	Condition
A.	4.2	Normal
B.	8.2	Alarm
C.	15	Dangerous
D.	30	Unknown

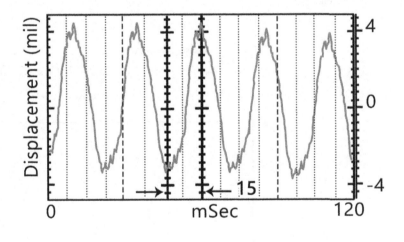

What is the amplitude of the next vibration waveform taken from a centrifugal pump? What is the condition of the pump? Alarm = 4 mm/sec rms. Select the best answer.

	Amplitude (mm/sec 0p)	Condition
A.	1.05	Normal
B.	2.10	Alarm
C.	15.0	Dangerous
D.	30.0	Unknown

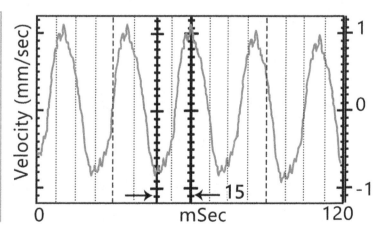

Acceptance Testing
Question 050

Use the next vibration data to evaluate the condition of a large pump (about 1000 hp, 1270 rpm). The set points are Alarm = 3.0 mils pp, Trip = 6.0 mils pp.

A. Acceptable

B. Warning

C. Danger

D. Condition is unknown

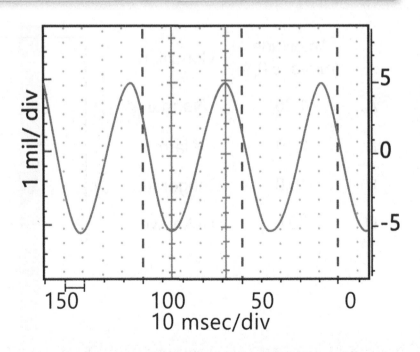

Use the next vibration data to evaluate the condition of a large pump (>1000 HP). The set points are Alarm = 2.4 g rms and Trip = 3.6 g rms. Select the best choice from the given answers.

A. Acceptable

B. Warning

C. Danger

D. Condition is unknown

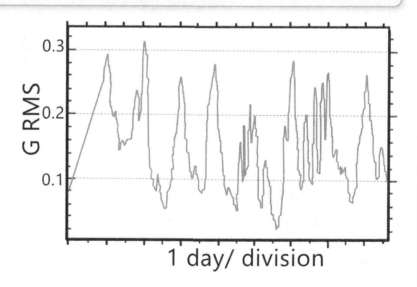

Acceptance Testing
Question 052

Use the next overall vibration trend to evaluate the condition of a large pump (>1000 H). The set points are Alarm = 0.24 ips rms and Trip = 0.36 ips rms.

A. Acceptable

B. Warning

C. Shutdown

D. Condition cannot be determined because of the method of calculation.

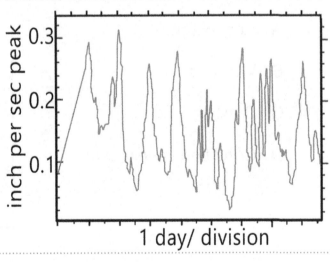

Note : ....

....

....

Use the next vibration data to evaluate the condition of a large compressor (>5000 HP). The set points are Alarm = 6 mils pp and Trip = 8 mils pp.

A. Acceptable

B. Warning

C. Danger

D. Condition is unknown without knowing the speed and vibration levels of other bearings.

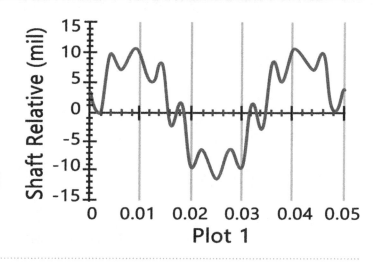

Plot 1

Note : ....

....

....

Question 054

Study the rms overall trend, which is for a large rotating machine. The data was collected by an online vibration monitoring sensor but the spectrum is unavailable. Use next table to evaluate the condition. What is the severity of the vibration?

A. Smooth

B. Normal

C. Surveillance

D. Unacceptable

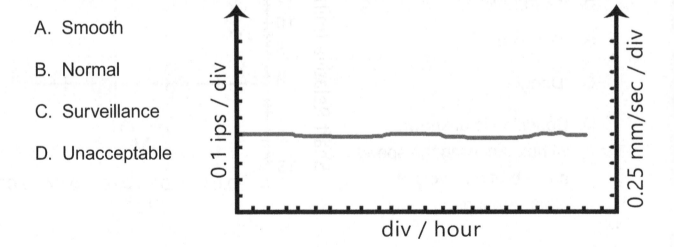

MACHINE SEVERITY	Overall Vibration Severity Guide (inch per second)	
	RMS	PEAK
Acceptable	Less than 0.08	Less than 0.16
Normal	0.08 to 0.12	0.16 to 0.24
Surveillance	0.12 to 0.28	0.24 to 0.7
Unacceptable	More than 0.28	More than 0.7

Note : ....

....

....

Acceptance Testing
Question 055

Use the next spectrum to evaluate the condition of a water pump (1790 rpm). High Alarm = 0.2 ips 0-p (5 mm/s 0p), High High Alarm = 0.4 ips 0-p (10 mm/s 0p)

A.	Normal condition.	C.	Dangerous condition.
B.	Surveillance condition.	D.	Evaluation cannot be determined without knowing the frequency.

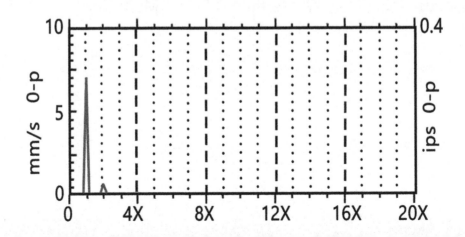

Use the next spectrum to evaluate the condition of a water pump (1790 rpm). Alert = 4 mm/sec rms, Danger = 6 mm/sec rms.

A.	Normal condition	C.	Shutdown condition
B.	Surveillance condition	D.	Evaluation cannot be done without knowing the shaft speed.

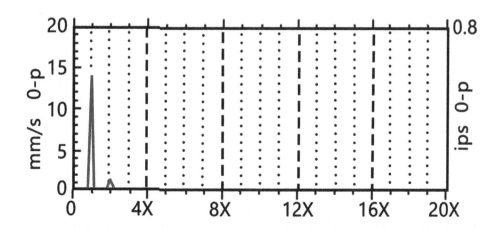

Acceptance Testing
Question 057

> **What is the amplitude of the next shaft vibration waveform? Based on the provided table, what is the condition of the machine?**

	Amplitude	Condition
A.	2 mil 0-p	Alarm
B.	2 mil p-p	Dangerous
C.	4 mil p-p	Dangerous
D.	120 mil 0-p	Dangerous

Note : ....

....

....

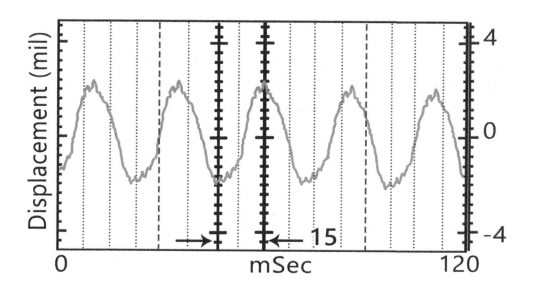

Below 1.5 mil pp	Normal
Between 1.5 to 3.0 mil pp	Alarm
Above 3.0 mil pp	Dangerous

Acceptance Testing
Question 058

Study the next vibration waveform. Based on the next criteria, what is the vibration severity? The data is taken from the bearing housing of a medium size motor. The acceptable limit is 0.20 ips 0-P.

A.	Normal condition.	C.	Unacceptable condition.
B.	Rejected because the signal is not symmetric.	D.	Condition cannot be determined.

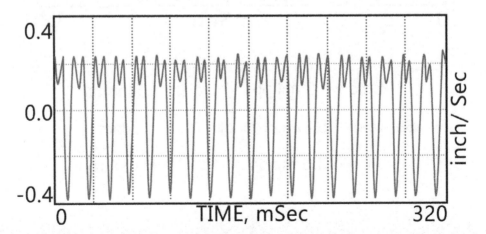

Consider a standard medium size (100 Hp or 75 kW) induction motor running at an unknown speed. What is the severity evaluation of a vibration amplitude at 0.2 ips 0-p purely at 2LF or 120 Hz based on the below table?

A. Normal condition

B. Surveillance condition

C. Unacceptable condition

D. Insufficient information is available

SEVERITY	Filtered Vibration Severity Guide for 1 X
	RMS (inch per second)
Acceptable	Less than 0.08
Normal	0.08 to 0.12
Surveillance	0.12 to 0.16
Unacceptable	More than 0.16

Question 060

Consider a small size (10 Hp or 7.5 kW) motor running at 1780 rpm. What is the severity evaluation of a vibration amplitude at 0.2 mm rms purely at 1X based on the next table?

A. Acceptable condition

B. Surveillance condition

C. Unacceptable condition

D. Insufficient information is available

Note : ....

....

....

SEVERITY	Filtered Vibration Severity Guide for 1 X	
	RMS (inch per second)	RMS (mm/sec)
Acceptable	Less than 0.08	Less than 2
Normal	0.08 to 0.12	2 to 3
Surveillance	0.12 to 0.28	3 to 7
Unacceptable	More than 0.28	More than 7

Note : ....

....

....

Acceptance Testing
Question 061

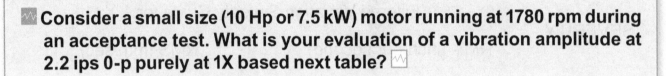

Consider a small size (10 Hp or 7.5 kW) motor running at 1780 rpm during an acceptance test. What is your evaluation of a vibration amplitude at 2.2 ips 0-p purely at 1X based next table?

A.	Normal condition
B.	Surveillance condition
C.	Unacceptable condition
D.	Insufficient information is available

Note : ....

....

....

SEVERITY	Filtered Vibration Severity Guide for 1 X	
	RMS (inch per second)	RMS (mm/sec)
Acceptable	Less than 0.08	Less than 2
Normal	0.08 to 0.12	2 to 3
Surveillance	0.12 to 0.28	3 to 7
Unacceptable	More than 0.28	More than 7

Note : ....

....

....

Acceptance Testing
Question 062

What is the condition of a DC motor whose vibration data is shown below? Assume you are performing an acceptance test and use the provided limits. Use a ruler for accurate answers.

A.	Normal condition.	C.	Unacceptable condition.
B.	Surveillance condition.	D.	It depends on the resolution of the spectrum.

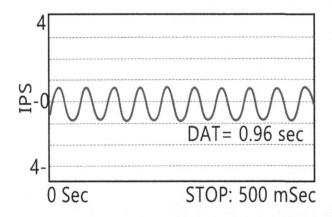

SEVERITY	Overall Vibration Severity Guide for Operating Speed Faults (inch per second)	
	RMS	PEAK
Acceptable	Less than 0.08	Less than 0.16
Normal	0.08 to 0.12	0.16 to 0.24
Surveillance	0.12 to 0.28	0.24 to 0.55
Unacceptable	More than 0.28	More than 0.55

Note : ....

....

....

Acceptance Testing
Question 063

Under what condition(s) can an analyst use the R/C method to evaluate the severity of a machine's vibration? Refer to the provided table and illustration. R is shaft vibration and C is the bearing clearance.

A. Machine's rotor must be mounted on journal bearings.

B. Vibration measured must be for a shaft relative vibration.

C. The rotor must be mounted on rolling element bearings and run between 600-3600 rpm.

D. A and B

Note : ....

....

....

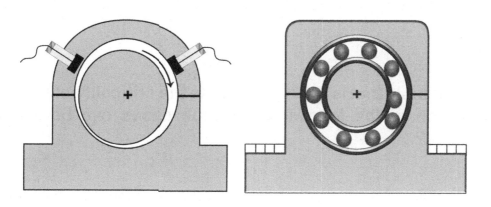

Vibration Severity	Shaft Vibration To Bearing Clearance Ratio = R/C
	Rotational Speed (600-3600 rpm)
Normal	Less than 0.3
Surveillance	0.3 to 0.5
Critical	0.5 to 0.7
Dangerous	More than 0.7

Acceptance Testing
Question 064

Study the given table that is used to evaluate the criticality of machinery vibration. Which of the following vibration cases can be evaluated using this table?

A. Vibration collected from a very small motor (less than 4 Hp or 3 kW)

B. Vibration collected from a large motor monitored by online eddy current probes.

C. Vibration collected from a shaft of a large motor with journal bearings.

D. Vibration collected from a large motor monitored by online displacement probes.

Note : ....

....

....

SEVERITY	Overall Vibration Severity Guide for Operating Speed Faults (inch per second)	
	RMS	PEAK
Acceptable	Less than 0.08	Less than 0.16
Normal	0.08 to 0.12	0.16 to 0.24
Surveillance	0.12 to 0.28	0.24 to 0.7
Unacceptable	More than 0.28	More than 0.7

Acceptance Testing
Question 065

Study the next table that is used to report the vibration severity of rotating equipment. Which of the following motors can be evaluated using this table? Both C and R are expressed in the same units.

A. A very small motor (smaller than 4 Hp or 3 kW) planned for replacement every 5 years.

B. A large motor with an online relative vibration monitoring system.

C. A large motor with ball bearings running at 900 rpm.

D. A large motor running at 3599 rpm and monitored by accelerometers.

Note : ....

....

....

Vibration Severity	Shaft Vibration To Bearing Clearance Ratio = R/C	Recommended Action
	Rotational Speed (600 to 3600 rpm)	
Normal	Less than 0.3	Routine Monitoring
Surveillance	0.3 to 0.5	Increase Monitoring
Critical	0.5 to 0.7	Plan for a Shutdown
Dangerous	More than 0.7	Shutdown Immediately

Question 066

Study the below table which is similar to an ISO standard for evaluating the condition of rotating machines. Which of the following vibration cases CANNOT be evaluated using this table?

A. Vibration collected from a very small motor (less than 4 Hp).

B. Vibration collected from a large motor by an online relative vibration monitoring.

C. Vibration collected from a large motor whose shaft is mounted on ball bearings.

D. Vibration collected from a medium motor monitored by accelerometers.

Vibration Severity	Shaft Vibration To Bearing Clearance Ratio = R/C		Recommended Action
	Low rpm 0 - 3600	High rpm 3601 - 10000	
Normal	Less than 0.3	Less than 0.2	Routine Monitoring
Surveillance	0.3 - 0.5	0.2 - 0.4	Diagnose and Increase Monitoring
Critical	0.5 - 0.7	0.4 - 0.6	Plan for a Shutdown
Dangerous	More than 0.7	More than 0.6	Shutdown Immediately

Acceptance Testing
Question 067

Study the next spectrum collected from a boiler feed water pump (5790 rpm). With the limited information provided, what is the condition of the pump based on the R/C limits? Use the bearing clearance as a basis. Data sheet shows that bearing clearance is 8-10 mils. To convert mil to micron, multiply by 25.

A. Normal condition

B. Surveillance condition

C. Between Surveillance and
   Unacceptable condition

D. Unacceptable condition

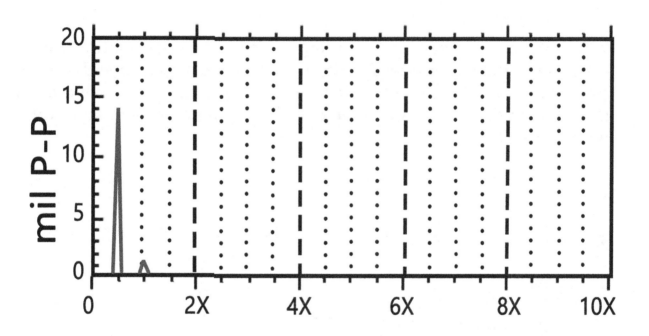

Note : ....

....

....

Question 068

What is the condition of large rotating equipment whose shaft vibration is shown in the next plot? Use the provided R/C table. Speed is 5005 rpm, power is 2000 Hp and the bearings are journal type having 8 mil clearance to the shaft. The amplitude (R) is from a non-contact probe in mil peak-to-peak.

A. Normal

B. Surveillance

C. Critical

D. The phase angle is needed for a proper evaluation

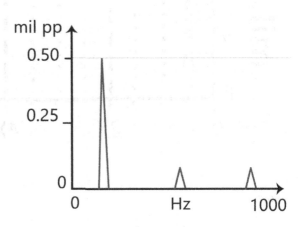

Vibration Severity	Shaft Vibration To Bearing Clearance Ratio = R/C
	Speed Range (3601- 10000 rpm)
Normal	Less than 0.2
Surveillance	0.2 to 0.4
Critical	0.4 to 0.6
Dangerous	Higher than 0.6

Note : ....

....

....

Acceptance Testing
Question 069

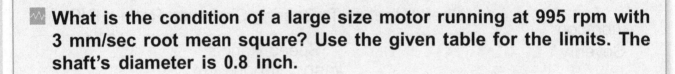 **What is the condition of a large size motor running at 995 rpm with 3 mm/sec root mean square? Use the given table for the limits. The shaft's diameter is 0.8 inch.**

A.	Excellent
B.	Satisfactory
C.	Unsatisfactory
D.	Unacceptable

Vibration Severity	Shaft Vibration To Bearing Clearance Ratio = R/C		Recommended Action
	Low rpm 0 - 3600 rpm	High rpm 3601 - 10000	
Normal	Less than 0.3	Less than 0.2	Routine Monitoring
Surveillance	0.3 - 0.5	0.2 - 0.4	Diagnose and Increase Monitoring
Critical	0.5 - 0.7	0.4 - 0.6	Plan for a Shutdown
Dangerous	More than 0.7	More than 0.6	Shutdown Immediately

Acceptance Testing
Question 070

Evaluate the condition of a 2 hp pump whose vibration readings are given as follows:

Inboard Horizontal =	0.03	Outboard Horizontal =	0.02
Inboard Vertical =	0.04	Outboard Vertical =	0.03
Inboard Axial =	0.03	Outboard Axial =	0.27

All units are inch per sec 0-P . Use the given table for the limits.

A. Insufficient data to evaluate.

B. Satisfactory

C. Unsatisfactory

D. Unacceptable

| Vibration Severity | Shaft Vibration To Bearing Clearance Ratio = R/C | | Recommended Action |
	Low rpm (0 - 3600)	High rpm (3601 - 10000)	
Normal	Less than 0.3	Less than 0.2	Routine Monitoring
Surveillance	0.3 - 0.5	0.2 - 0.4	Diagnose and Increase Monitoring
Critical	0.5 - 0.7	0.4 - 0.6	Plan for a Shutdown
Dangerous	More than 0.7	More than 0.6	Shutdown Immediately

Acceptance Testing
Question 071

Assume you are performing an acceptance tests. Evaluate the condition of a huge horizontal motor whose vibration readings are given as follows:

Inboard Horizontal = 2.3 Outboard Horizontal In board = 2.2
Inboard Vertical =   2.4 Outboard Vertical In board =   1.7
Inboard Axial =   2.0 Outboard Axial =   2.7

The motor is installed on a heavy concrete foundation. All units are in mm/sec rms. Use the given table.

A.	Good	C.	Unsatisfactory
B.	Satisfactory	D.	Unacceptable

Class IV Large Machine Rigid foundation	Vibration Velocity rms (inches/sec)	Vibration Velocity rms (mm/sec)
Unacceptable	1.77	44.958
	1.1	27.94
Unsatisfactory	0.71	18.034
Unsatisfactory	0.48	12.192
Satisfactory	0.28	7.112
Satisfactory	0.18	4.572
Good	0.11	2.794
Good	0.07	1.778
Good	0.04	1.016
Good	0.03	0.762
	0.02	0.508
	0.01	0.254

Question 072

Study next unfiltered vibration plot (collected from a large centrifugal pump) and Table 1, 2 and 3. No spectrum is avialble to idenify the frequencies and filtered amplitudes. Based on the given information, which evaluation table is the most applicable to use for this case?

A.	Table 1	C.	Table 3
B.	Table 2	D.	None of the three tables is valid for this case.

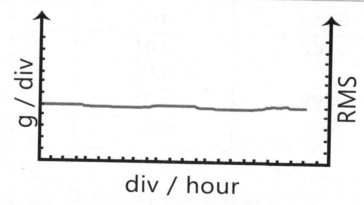

Table 1 SEVERITY	Shaft Vibration To Bearing Clearance Ratio = R/C
	Low Speed 0 to 3600 rpm
Normal	Less than 0.3
Surveillance	0.3 to 0.5
Dangerous	More than 0.5

Table 2 SEVERITY	Overall Vibration (inch/second rms)
Acceptable	Less than 0.08
Surveillance	0.12 to 0.28
Unacceptable	More than 0.28

Table 3 SEVERITY	Overall Vibration (inch/second peak)
Acceptable	Less than 0.30
Surveillance	0.30 to 0.7
Unacceptable	More than 0.7

Acceptance Testing
Question 073

Study next unfiltered vibration plot (collected from a large centrifugal pump) and Table 1, 2 and 3. No spectrum is avialble to idenify the frequencies and filtered amplitudes. Based on the given information, which evaluation table is the most applicable to use for this case?

A.	Table 1	C.	Table 3
B.	Table 2	D.	All of the tables can be used for this case.

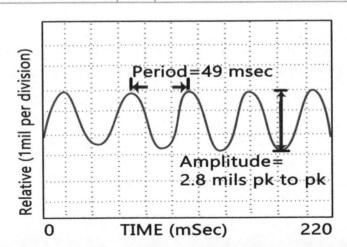

Table 1 SEVERITY	Shaft Vibration To Bearing Clearance Ratio = R/C
	Low Speed 0 to 3600 rpm
Normal	Less than 0.3
Surveillance	0.3 to 0.5
Dangerous	More than 0.5

Table 2 SEVERITY	Overall Vibration (inch/second rms)
Acceptable	Less than 0.08
Surveillance	0.12 to 0.28
Unacceptable	More than 0.28

Table 3 SEVERITY	Overall Vibration (inch/second peak)
Acceptable	Less than 0.30
Surveillance	0.30 to 0.7
Unacceptable	More than 0.7

Question 074

Study next unfiltered vibration plot (collected from a large centrifugal pump) and Table 1, 2 and 3. No spectrum is avialble to idenify the frequencies and filtered amplitudes. Based on the given information, which evaluation table is the most applicable to use for this case?

A.	Table 1	C.	Table 3
B.	Table 2	D.	All of the tables can be used for this case.

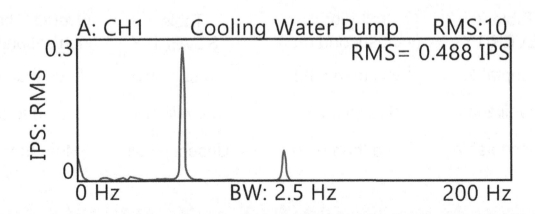

Table 1 SEVERITY	Shaft Vibration To Bearing Clearance Ratio = R/C
	Low Speed 0 to 3600 rpm
Normal	Less than 0.3
Surveillance	0.3 to 0.5
Dangerous	More than 0.5

Table 2 SEVERITY	Overall Vibration (inch/second rms)
Acceptable	Less than 0.08
Surveillance	0.12 to 0.28
Unacceptable	More than 0.28

Table 3 SEVERITY	Overall Vibration (inch/second peak)
Acceptable	Less than 0.30
Surveillance	0.30 to 0.7
Unacceptable	More than 0.7

Acceptance Testing
Question 075

Study the belwo zero-peak vibration trend and Table 1, 2 and 3. Evaluate the condition of the vibration data (collected from a large centrifugal pump). Which evaluation table is the most applicable to use for this case?

A.	Table 1	C.	Table 3
B.	Table 2	D.	All of the tables can be used for this case.

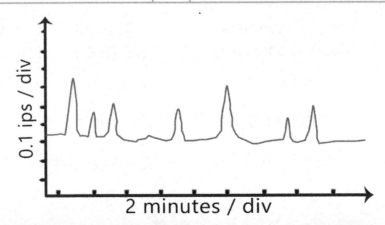

Table 1 SEVERITY	Shaft Vibration To Bearing Clearance Ratio = R/C
	Low Speed 0 to 3600 rpm
Normal	Less than 0.3
Surveillance	0.3 to 0.5
Dangerous	More than 0.5

Table 2 SEVERITY	Overall Vibration (inch/second rms)
Acceptable	Less than 0.08
Surveillance	0.12 to 0.28
Unacceptable	More than 0.28

Table 3 SEVERITY	Overall Vibration (inch/second peak)
Acceptable	Less than 0.30
Surveillance	0.30 to 0.7
Unacceptable	More than 0.7

Acceptance Testing
Question 076

What is the condition evaluation of a centrifugal compressor based on its shaft vibration shown in the next plot? The shaft is mounted on journal bearings whose clearance is 10 mils. The probes (on the same bearing) are 100° a part. The alarm settings are 40 % and 60 % of bearing clearance. Notice that 1 mil ≈ 25 microns.

A. Acceptable condition

B. Surveillance condition

C. Unacceptable condition

D. The provided data is not enough. Phase angle and shaft speed are needed.

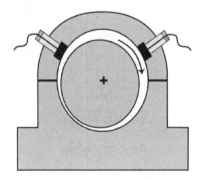

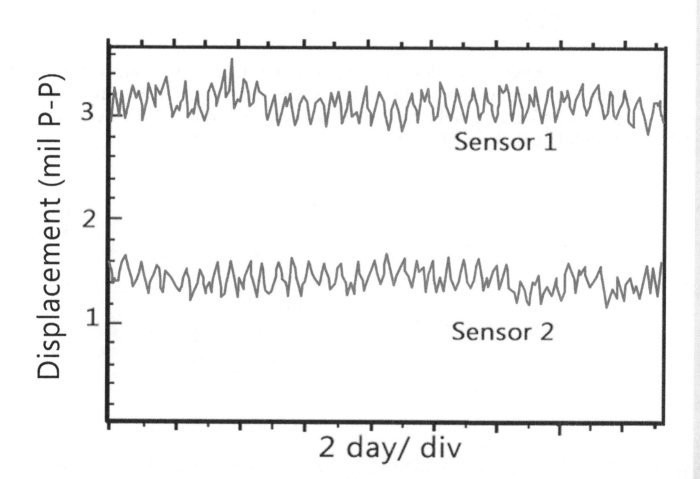

Acceptance Testing
Question 077

Study the next illustration for a centrifugal pump (between bearing). What is the condition of the pump based on the given information? All readings are in inch/sec 0-p. This pump has come from overhaul. Acceptance limit is 0.08 ips, peak.

A. Acceptable

B. Keep under monitoring

C. Rejected

D. More information is needed

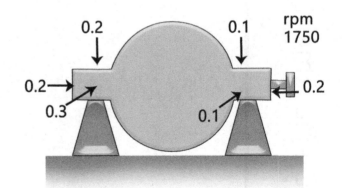

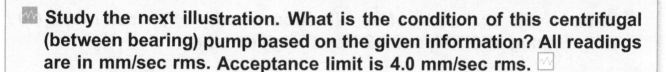

Study the next illustration. What is the condition of this centrifugal (between bearing) pump based on the given information? All readings are in mm/sec rms. Acceptance limit is 4.0 mm/sec rms.

A. Acceptable

B. Keep under monitoring

C. Rejected

D. More information is needed.

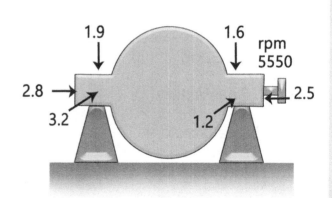

Note : ....
....
....

Acceptance Testing
Question 079

What is your evaluation of the vibration severity of a small motor (10 kW) running at 0.55 ips rms? Use the given table.

A.	Good
B.	Satisfactory
C.	Unsatisfactory
D.	Unacceptable

Note : ....

....

....

Type of Machine				Velocity Vibration Amplitude	
Small Machines < 15 kW	Medium Machines 15 < kW < 75	Large Machines > 75 kW		inches/sec rms	mm/sec rms
		Heavy/Normal foundation	Special foundation		
Unacceptable	Unacceptable	Unacceptable	Unacceptable	1.77	44.958
				1.1	27.94
			Unsatisfactory	0.71	18.034
		Unsatisfactory	Unsatisfactory	0.48	12.192
	Unsatisfactory	Unsatisfactory	Satisfactory	0.28	7.112
Unsatisfactory	Unsatisfactory	Satisfactory	Satisfactory	0.18	4.572
	Satisfactory	Satisfactory	Good	0.11	2.8
Satisfactory	Satisfactory	Good	Good	0.07	1.778
	Good	Good	Good	0.04	1.016
Good	Good	Good	Good	0.03	0.75
				0.02	0.508
				0.01	0.254

ANSWER SHEETS

EMPTY ANSWER SHEET 1

1	A	B	C	D
2	A	B	C	D
3	A	B	C	D
4	A	B	C	D
5	A	B	C	D
6	A	B	C	D
7	A	B	C	D
8	A	B	C	D
9	A	B	C	D
10	A	B	C	D
11	A	B	C	D
12	A	B	C	D
13	A	B	C	D
14	A	B	C	D
15	A	B	C	D

16	A	B	C	D
17	A	B	C	D
18	A	B	C	D
19	A	B	C	D
20	A	B	C	D
21	A	B	C	D
22	A	B	C	D
23	A	B	C	D
24	A	B	C	D
25	A	B	C	D
26	A	B	C	D
27	A	B	C	D
28	A	B	C	D
29	A	B	C	D
30	A	B	C	D

EMPTY ANSWER SHEET 1

31	A	B	C	D
32	A	B	C	D
33	A	B	C	D
34	A	B	C	D
35	A	B	C	D
36	A	B	C	D
37	A	B	C	D
38	A	B	C	D
39	A	B	C	D
40	A	B	C	D
41	A	B	C	D
42	A	B	C	D
43	A	B	C	D
44	A	B	C	D
45	A	B	C	D

46	A	B	C	D
47	A	B	C	D
48	A	B	C	D
49	A	B	C	D
50	A	B	C	D
51	A	B	C	D
52	A	B	C	D
53	A	B	C	D
54	A	B	C	D
55	A	B	C	D
56	A	B	C	D
57	A	B	C	D
58	A	B	C	D
59	A	B	C	D
60	A	B	C	D

EMPTY ANSWER SHEET 1

61	A	B	C	D
62	A	B	C	D
63	A	B	C	D
64	A	B	C	D
65	A	B	C	D
66	A	B	C	D
67	A	B	C	D
68	A	B	C	D
69	A	B	C	D
70	A	B	C	D
71	A	B	C	D
72	A	B	C	D
73	A	B	C	D
74	A	B	C	D
75	A	B	C	D

76	A	B	C	D
77	A	B	C	D
78	A	B	C	D
79	A	B	C	D

Notes

EMPTY ANSWER SHEET 2

1	A	B	C	D
2	A	B	C	D
3	A	B	C	D
4	A	B	C	D
5	A	B	C	D
6	A	B	C	D
7	A	B	C	D
8	A	B	C	D
9	A	B	C	D
10	A	B	C	D
11	A	B	C	D
12	A	B	C	D
13	A	B	C	D
14	A	B	C	D
15	A	B	C	D

16	A	B	C	D
17	A	B	C	D
18	A	B	C	D
19	A	B	C	D
20	A	B	C	D
21	A	B	C	D
22	A	B	C	D
23	A	B	C	D
24	A	B	C	D
25	A	B	C	D
26	A	B	C	D
27	A	B	C	D
28	A	B	C	D
29	A	B	C	D
30	A	B	C	D

EMPTY ANSWER SHEET 2

31	A	B	C	D
32	A	B	C	D
33	A	B	C	D
34	A	B	C	D
35	A	B	C	D
36	A	B	C	D
37	A	B	C	D
38	A	B	C	D
39	A	B	C	D
40	A	B	C	D
41	A	B	C	D
42	A	B	C	D
43	A	B	C	D
44	A	B	C	D
45	A	B	C	D

46	A	B	C	D
47	A	B	C	D
48	A	B	C	D
49	A	B	C	D
50	A	B	C	D
51	A	B	C	D
52	A	B	C	D
53	A	B	C	D
54	A	B	C	D
55	A	B	C	D
56	A	B	C	D
57	A	B	C	D
58	A	B	C	D
59	A	B	C	D
60	A	B	C	D

EMPTY ANSWER SHEET 2

61	A	B	C	D
62	A	B	C	D
63	A	B	C	D
64	A	B	C	D
65	A	B	C	D
66	A	B	C	D
67	A	B	C	D
68	A	B	C	D
69	A	B	C	D
70	A	B	C	D
71	A	B	C	D
72	A	B	C	D
73	A	B	C	D
74	A	B	C	D
75	A	B	C	D

76	A	B	C	D
77	A	B	C	D
78	A	B	C	D
79	A	B	C	D

Notes

ANSWER KEY

ANSWER KEY

Q. #	Answer
1	A
2	D
3	D
4	C
5	C
6	C
7	A
8	D
9	A
10	A
11	A
12	D
13	D
14	D
15	D

Q. #	Answer
16	A
17	A
18	A
19	A
20	D
21	D
22	A
23	A
24	C
25	B
26	A
27	A
28	D
29	C
30	B

Q. #	Answer
31	B
32	D
33	D
34	D
35	D
36	B
37	A
38	B
39	A
40	B
41	C
42	B
43	B
44	A
45	B

Q. #	Answer
46	B
47	A
48	B
49	A
50	C
51	A
52	D
53	C
54	D
55	B
56	C
57	C
58	C
59	C
60	A

ANSWER KEY

Q. #	Answer
61	C
62	C
63	D
64	A
65	B
66	B
67	D
68	A
69	B
70	A
71	A
72	D
73	A
74	B
75	C

Q. #	Answer
76	A
77	C
78	A
79	D

Notes

ORDER OTHER PARTS OF CAT I PREP I PACKAGE

Don't guess where your skill stands; certify it. PrepCertify believes that the best preparation for professional certifications is obtained through practicing well-designed real world problems.

Learn what really matters in real world industry while mastering the Body of Knowledge in the certification standards. Your Cat I Prep I series does that for you. Through PrepCertify, you will achieve your certification in a much shorter time and with a greater value of your time and effort.

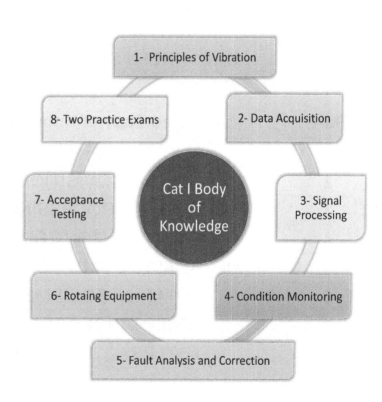

Vibration Analysis Certification Exam Preparation Package
Certified Vibration Analyst Category I
ISO 18436-2 CVA Level 1
CAT I PREP I SERIES PRACTICE TESTS

Part	Covered Body of Knowledge	ISBN-13
1	PRINCIPLES OF VIBRATION	978-1-64415-006-1
2	DATA ACQUISITION	978-1-64415-009-2
3	SIGNAL PROCESSING	978-1-64415-002-3
4	CONDITION MONITORING	978-1-64415-005-4
5	FAULT ANALYSIS AND CORRECTION	978-1-64415-008-5
6	ROTATING EQUIPMENT	978-1-64415-014-6
7	ACCEPTANCE TESTING	978-1-64415-004-7
8	TWO PRACTICE TESTS	978-1-64415-007-8

Notes

Notes

Made in the USA
Coppell, TX
12 January 2024

27630906R00083